COLNE VALLEY CLOTH

NIGHT IN THE COLNE VALLEY

COLNE VALLEY CLOTH

FROM THE EARLIEST TIMES

TO THE PRESENT DAY

BY

PHYLLIS BENTLEY

WITH ILLUSTRATIONS BY

HAROLD BLACKBURN

ISSUED BY

THE HUDDERSFIELD AND DISTRICT

WOOLLEN EXPORT GROUP

PRINTED IN ENGLAND
AT THE CURWEN PRESS, PLAISTOW, LONDON, E.13

CONTENTS

I.   Wool and Water   *page* 5
II. Home and Market   18
III. Machines and Men   35
IV. Colour and Design   55
V.   Quality Tells   62

LIST OF ILLUSTRATIONS

Night in the Colne Valley, 1947   *frontispiece*
A West Riding Beck   *page* 5
Map of England showing the Colne Valley   7
The Pennines: West Riding Scenery   8
A Walke Mylne   11
Fulling Stocks   11
King's Mill, 1944   12
Cropper's Shears   14
Spinning from the Distaff   15
'Wuzzing' Skep and Bar   16
Map of the Colne Valley District   *facing* 16
Weaver's Cottage   18
Map of the Colne Valley: Home and Market   19
Clothier going to Market   20
Pack-horse Bridge   21
Marketing Cloth, Huddersfield Parish Church, 1671 22
Children Carding Wool   24
Spinster at the Great Wheel   24
Handthrown shuttle, seventeenth-century Loom   25

Stretching a wet kersey on the tenter   *page* 26
Deanhead, an old weaving hamlet   29
Business in the Cloth Hall, Huddersfield   32
An eighteenth-century Clothier's Pattern Book   *facing* 32
Estimating the width of the corridor   33
Kay's Flying Shuttle, 1733   35
Yeoman Clothier and his family at work   37
Outsteps at High Kinders, Greenfield   39
Cog Hole: last water-driven scribbling mill   40
Cloth Dressing: Interior of a Cropping Shop   42
John Wood's Cropping Shop   44
'Old Enoch'   46
Horsfall's route on the day of his murder   47
Ottiwells Mills, Marsden, 1812   48
Geology of the Woollen District   50
Factory Children of 1826   51
Richard Oastler   52
Advent of Tweeds among the Sporting Fraternity   55
Colne Valley Quality   62
Map of the Colne Valley, Present Day   64
View across the Colne Valley at Milnsbridge   66
Sir John Ramsden's Canal   69

'Night in The Colne Valley' is reproduced by courtesy of
The Yorkshire Post.

A tumbling beck amid the heather and bracken

I. WOOL AND WATER

CLOTH has been woven of wool in the Colne Valley for at least six centuries.

It may, indeed, have been woven there for nearly twelve centuries, for as far back as A.D. 796 the great Emperor Charlemagne over in France wrote to King Offa to ask him to see that the woollen cloaks sent to France might be made the same as used to come in the olden time. As King Offa then ruled over the north-midland part of England, which includes what we now call the West Riding of Yorkshire, where the Colne Valley lies, the cloth in Charlemagne's cloaks may have come from some weaver's cottage on the Golcar hillside. However, we will make no claims for the Colne Valley which we cannot substantiate, so we will

5

claim only the six hundred years which we can prove by records.

England, that green and pleasant land of grass, has always been a wool-growing country. Long before the Norman Conquest in 1066 wool was exported from England to the continent of Europe, and in the Middle Ages the monks of England had dealings in wool with customers as far afield as Flanders and Northern Italy. England's wealth, her trade, her politics, her traditions of craftsmanship and freedom, have all been built upon the sheep. (In 1303 Earl Lacy owned 3,000 sheep in Yorkshire.) That the Lord Chancellor of England sits today on a Woolsack is not just a piece of nonsensical frippery, but a relic of the days when the clip from England's sheep was her main export, which paid her taxes and created trade treaties and, if need be, made loans to her kings to furnish armies, or redeemed a pawned crown. As an inscription above a merchant's house in the West of England, built in the Middle Ages, runs:

> 'I praise God and ever shall
> It is the sheep hath paid for all'.

How did it happen that this particular district of England about which we are writing, the West Riding of Yorkshire, became the centre of the cloth trade? It is a small stretch of country, tucked away in hills, not very conveniently situated as regards ports and railways; how did it achieve a world-wide reputation? Its greatness is chiefly due to its geography and its climate; to the rocks beneath the West Riding man's feet and the air above his head.

Rolling down the middle of England, from the Lake District in the north to the Peak in Derbyshire, runs a range of interlocking spurs of hills called the Pennine Chain—the backbone of England, as we who live amongst these hills like to think of them. The geology of these hills varies. In the north of Yorkshire they are composed of white limestone, on

A·MAP·OF·ENGLAND·SHOWING
THE·COLNE·VALLEY·CLOTH·DISTRICT

which grows short sweet grass, very green, very good for eating by long-woolled sheep. But there are few springs, few streams, on limestone rock, and the limestone water is harsh to fibres though kind to children's teeth. Below these limestone hills comes a sudden break in the Chain, the Aire gap,

7

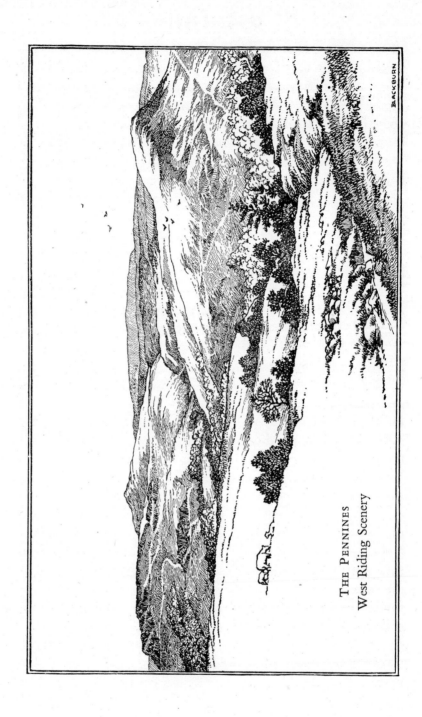

THE PENNINES
West Riding Scenery

BLACKBURN

through which the River Aire flows, just north of Skipton. South of that gap there is no more limestone; the hills are composed of rock called millstone grit, with a fringe of coal measure. Now this hard, dark, millstone grit, which is often coated with peat or clay, does not grow rich grass or good crops. It cannot pasture many cows, it cannot grow fields of waving corn; oats, and sparse coarse grass, which short-haired sheep can feed on, are its only products. Both coal and grit country, however, are rich in springs and streams; so here the hillsides are seamed by countless deep and narrow valleys, each with its tumbling thread of water. Rough, sweeping, interlocking hills, crowned with dark rocks and purple heather, with many cold, rocky little 'becks', as Yorkshire folk call streams, rushing swiftly down from the moorland through the fields to the little river in the steep, wooded, winding valley below—that is the scenery of the West Riding. You are scarcely ever out of the sound of falling water. This water contains no lime, it is soft and kind to fibres. Nor does it often fail, for the great winds which sweep across the Atlantic, moisture-laden, strike the Pennine Hills and dissolve into abundant rain. On the west side of the hills, in Lancashire, the rain is so abundant that the cotton fibre can be woven in the moist air. On the eastern slopes, in Yorkshire, the rain is somewhat less, so that it does not rot the sheep's hoofs and wool, but it is still plentiful.

Wool, then, and soft water—those two prime necessities of the cloth trade—were plentiful in the West Riding of Yorkshire. Coal lurked beneath the soil, which we shall need to speak of later; while not very far away, to the south of the county, were beds of precious iron ore. As there was not much of a living to be won by farming the inhospitable land, and the wool and the water were close at hand, the dwellers in this West Riding began to make for sale what in those far-off days many households made for their own use—woven woollen cloth.

The Colne is one of the small rivers I have spoken of above. Winding down the Colne Valley from the Pennine Heights, fed as it goes by innumerable becks pouring from the hills on its flanks down clefts which we call 'sykes' and 'cloughs', it joins the Calder, a rather larger but similar stream, as it reaches the plain.

The first we hear of any part of the Colne Valley district in recorded history is a mention in 1086 of Golcar, Huddersfield and Almondbury, which were then written Guldeagscar, Odersfelt and Almanberie. After William of Normandy conquered England in 1066, he sent commissioners round the country to note down all about the land, its crops and stocks and buildings, its water-mills and pastures and fishponds, who owned it, and who paid rent. These details were all set down in Domesday Book, which formed a kind of gigantic rent roll and estate book for the whole country. At that time it seems that the Colne Valley was thickly forested, for a few years later it was said that a squirrel could travel the seven miles from Marsden down to Huddersfield leaping from branch to branch, without putting foot to the ground, while stags were hunted in the Marsden forest for more than two hundred years after the Conquest. William the Conqueror divided the land of England between his nobles, who had come over with him on the invasion from Normandy; the Colne Valley was part of the estate of one of these, Ilbert de Lacy.

I have mentioned William the Conqueror and his Norman barons because to understand the story of the West Riding cloth trade it is necessary to know something of the way the Normans ruled. King William did not give away the land for nothing, naturally; he rented it, and the barons paid, not in money but in service; they were bound to provide so many armed men to follow him so many days a year. The barons rented parcels of land to their knights, on similar though lesser terms, and so it went on down the scale to

Primitive method of fulling
The Walke Mylne

the simple people, amongst whose duties came that of having their corn ground and their cloth fulled at the lord of the manor's water-mill, paying him in money or kind for this service. I am writing this for textile manufacturers, who do not need to be told what 'fulling' means, but in case some others chance to read it let me explain that fulling or milling a woollen cloth is pounding it until the fibres of the wool hook closely into each other, and the cloth becomes thickened and felted and has sufficient substance. At first this was done by trampling on it with the feet, so that a man who fulled cloth was often called a 'walker'; later cloth was fulled by vertically falling stocks, that is, big wooden hammers which beat on it. The lord of the manor owned the fulling mill,

The fulling stocks

11

The King's Mill, 1944
Site of the manorial corn and fulling mills on the River Colne

which was also the corn mill; it ran by water-wheel, and he built it, naturally, in the valley, where the stream was big enough to give a good force of water. Such a fulling mill was built by the Lacys at the foot of the Colne Valley, near Huddersfield. Later, through various marriages, the lands of the Lacys fell into the hands of the crown, and this fulling mill became the King's Mill. This fulling mill was already in existence before 1340; a modern textile factory stands on the site and is still called the King's Mill today. Down to this King's Mill in the valley, and later to other water-mills like it, the cloth weavers on the hills around in Norman times brought their cloth to be scoured and fulled.

In England in the Middle Ages a person was given a second name often either from the place where he lived or from his trade. So in the West Riding of Yorkshire people were called John Sykes or John Clough, meaning John who lived beside a stream or John who lived in a cleft in the hill—there are hundreds of people called Sykes in the Huddersfield district today. So, too, there were men called Thomas

Webster, or Ralph Fuller, or Gilbert Lister, or John Walker.
A webster is a weaver, a lister is a dyer, a walker is the same
as a fuller. Whenever we meet these names in old records,
then, we know that cloth manufacturing was being carried
on. The Norman barons held law courts for their tenants to
settle their disputes, the Norman kings exacted taxes from
the people, and the records of these cases and taxes were
carefully and accurately kept, just as they would be today.
Wills, too, were carefully preserved. Now the wills and the
records of cases and taxes in Yorkshire, from the thirteenth
century onwards, are full of these textile trade names. We
meet Roger the Fuller of Holme acting as a juryman in 1274
and being in trouble the following year for 'four beasts
escaping'. Ralph Fuller pays a tax on eight sheep in 1297,
Thomas Webster is in trouble for letting his donkey stray
in 1275; William Fuller has a little trouble about his rent in
1277, Gilbert the Lister is fined in 1307, though history doesn't
relate for what offence, while John the Walker of Holme has
unlawfully detained two stones of wool in the same year.
Unluckily the Lacys' Court records, which include the
narrow strip of actual Colne Valley land, have not been
preserved, so that we can usually only catch glimpses of
Colne Valley folk in this period when they are paying taxes
or in litigation with people outside the valley. Thus we find
John the Dyer of Almondbury paying a ninth of his goods
in 1297, William Walker of Crosland paying fourpence tax
in 1379, while in 1316 we meet John Walker of Gouthe-
lakkers, that is, Golcar.

When, therefore, historians state that King Edward III,
who reigned from 1327 to 1377, introduced the cloth trade
into England, they are entirely wrong, for the cloth trade
existed in England at least a hundred years before he came
to the throne. Indeed, in the parish church of my own native
town in Yorkshire, Halifax, there stands a gravestone of
the date of 1150, on which is engraved quite clearly and

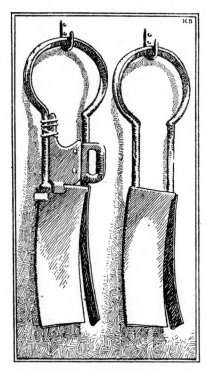

unmistakably a pair of cropper's shears—that is, a pair of the shears with which a clothdresser in the days before machinery cropped his cloth by hand. But to say that Edward encouraged the cloth trade and caused it to increase enormously is true enough. He persuaded Parliament to pass a law prohibiting the importation of foreign cloth, which it was declared should be worn by none but the King and Queen and their children; he forbade the export of English wool without special licence, and—most important of all—he invited many skilled clothiers from Flanders to come and reside in England, with their goods

Cropper's Shears, perfectly kept and still hanging in the factory where more than a century ago they were in use; mute evidence of a local pride in skill

and chattels and servants and apprentices, promising them many privileges if they would do so. Seventy families took advantage of this offer in the first year after it was made, two settling at York in the Yorkshire plain and carrying on their trade there. These Flemish clothiers taught us to spin a greater length of yarn from a pound of wool, and so much finer yarn than we had managed to achieve before, and other refinements of the cloth trade. These Flemings, says an old book called *The Golden Fleece*, 'shifted their residence according to the facility with which they could obtain water or fuel, or the material on which they worked'—that is, they sought the districts where they could find wool and wood and water. Accordingly we find a Simon Fleming appearing on a tax record in Almondbury in 1379. But I do not think the Flemings ever came in great numbers to the Colne Valley or the other uplands of the West Riding. These skilled craftsmen would have scorned the rough 'kerseys', narrow cloths, of white or plain crude colours, rough and uneven in texture, short in length, which were what we chiefly made at that time. They preferred East Anglia and the West of England or York, where there were already great guilds of cloth-workers, much more skilled at that time than our West Riding weavers.

As wool was no longer to leave the kingdom without a special licence, the King's revenue dropped, for he had hitherto drawn a fee on every outward-going sack of wool, as well as on every incoming yard of cloth. To make up for the loss of this, Parliament in 1353 granted him a subsidy of fourpence on each cloth offered for sale. This subsidy was collected at the same time as the cloth was measured by an official to see that it was the right breadth and length. The fee of this official, a halfpenny a cloth, was called Ulnage, from the old measure of length called an ell, and he himself was called the Ulnager. The local Ulnager was an important personage, and his post was a profitable one. He measured the cloth on a long stone table, then affixed a lead seal, stamped with its length. In the early days of the industry this Ulnage

Spinning from the distaff

15

The 'wuzzing' skep and bar
A primitive method of extracting
water from wool

ceremony was usually performed at the fulling mill after the cloth had been shrunk by fulling; later, as the trade grew, the Ulnager would call at the houses of the more important clothiers or seal the cloths at the market. The kerseys caused a great deal of trouble at first because they were so short they escaped the tax, which was obviously unfair. In 1393 this was altered, and any weaver was allowed to make and offer for sale cloths 'of such length and breadth as him shall please', provided he paid tax proportionately. The kerseys, which were a quarter the length of the better cloths, paid a penny each as tax. It was not till nearly three hundred years later that this tax was abolished, and the Ulnagers and the clothiers were always apt to quarrel with each other about the tax throughout that time. The records of their disputes prove to us the continued existence of the cloth trade.

In these early days, the market for the Colne Valley district cloth was on the hill-top at Almondbury. A descendant of Ilbert de Lacy secured a licence from the King to hold a market in Almondbury every Monday, in 1294, and to Almondbury the Colne Valley weavers took their weekly pieces. There chances to be a record preserved of the number of cloths sealed by the Ulnager in Almondbury for the two years 1473-1475. The number recorded is 427. This means whole cloths which paid fourpence, or their equivalent, that is, four kerseys. All the Almondbury cloths at that time would be kerseys, so this means that 1,708 kerseys were sealed in Almondbury in two years. The average for one year was therefore 854. A weaver could weave rather more than a cloth a week when he gave himself to it, but then so often he did not give himself wholly to his weaving. He made hay, or churned, or sowed his oats instead. Besides, he had to fetch and carry his wool and his cloth to and from the market, and supervise the oiling and carding and spinning, and set up his warp, and perhaps wait a day or two for his fulling till the river was running strongly enough to turn the water-wheel at the fulling mill, if the season was dry, as well. If we say that about twenty-one weavers were weaving and selling their goods in Almondbury market in 1475, that is forty pieces a year each, perhaps we shall not be far wrong.

It is a small beginning to an industry which has lined the banks of the Colne with huge textile factories. But then, 1475 is a long time ago. A good deal of water has flowed down the Colne, a good deal of wool has been spun in the Colne Valley, in five hundred years.

A typical weaver's cottage in the Pennines

II. HOME AND MARKET

DURING the next two centuries, 1500-1700, the West Riding cloth trade grew and flourished, but continued in the same type of organization. It was still domestic, carried on at home, and still an adjunct to farming. A man was granted leave to 'intake' a piece of upland moor, he cleared it and put it under grass and oats, gradually built a homestead and bought a horse and a cow, and paid for all this by weaving. His little holding of land perhaps just sufficed to feed his family but could do no more because of its harsh nature; his loom paid for rent, more intake, and any luxuries. One of his sons perhaps repeated the intake process higher up the moor, so that the strip of cleared land between windy moor and wooded valley steadily broadened. Such men we call yeoman clothiers, master clothiers, and almost every weaver

18

in the West Riding during this period was in this sense a master clothier. He owned his own loom, and wove in his own home, whether his holding of land was large or small. Gradually, as the weaving of cloth brought wealth to the uplands, cloth became more, and land less, important.

The clothier's home stood below the brow of the hill beside one of the tumbling streams he needed for his trade. His house, formerly of timbered oak, was now built of the strong local stone, the hard grey millstone grit, and stood two storeys high. The upper storey held the loom, and to give the weaver light as he sat at his work, this loom-chamber was built with a long row of mullioned windows—sometimes six or seven windows, sometimes in a larger homestead as many as fourteen or nineteen. Through these windows could be heard, as one passed from one house round the fold of the hill to the next, the thud of the treadles and the clack of the shuttle—the sound of the weaver at his loom.

But today the shuttle is silent in all the folds of the Colne Valley hills, for it is Market Day, and our clothier is going to market to sell his weekly piece. In the room below the loom-chamber stands a big stone hearth and a large wooden chest; the latter is the meal ark, it holds the oatmeal on which the clothier chiefly lives. His wife is already astir, baking an

Clothier going to market

oatcake on the backstone of the hearth, and some other of the long porous flexible oatcakes hang over a rack to dry by the fire.

Our weaver breaks his fast on porridge and oatcake and perhaps a slice from the cured ham hanging from the rafters. Then he saddles the donkey browsing by the door, throws his piece over its back, mounts himself behind, and sets off along the rough stone lane towards Almondbury. After a mile or two he overtakes one of

An old pack-horse bridge

his neighbours, a man less well furnished with this world's goods, who is carrying his piece over his shoulder, his arm held akimbo to support it. In a few more miles he himself is overtaken by a richer neighbour, who owns a sturdy horse. Each in turn crosses a narrow stone bridge, gracefully arched, with low parapets; this is a pack-horse bridge, the parapets are purposely built low so that the cloth on horseback may swing safely over them.

What year is it? It might be any year between 1500 and 1700. Perhaps it is 1552, and Parliament has passed an Act regulating the weight of wool to be put into each length of cloth; perhaps it is 1612 and a great lawsuit is being tried between the Yorkshire clothiers and the local Ulnagers.

21

Marketing cloth in the churchyard, Huddersfield Parish Church, 1671

Perhaps it is 1643, and King and Parliament are at war and fighting all over the county, so that trade is very bad; in that case our clothier is thinking soberly how much money he can spare to send to the Parliament's Yorkshire general, Fairfax. The Royalists, he has heard, are firing on the West Riding town of Bradford, whose clothiers, on the Parliament's side to a man, have hung sacks of wool round the church tower to protect it. Perhaps it is 1666, and Parliament has just enacted that every person shall be buried in a woollen shroud, for the good of the cloth trade, which has recently experienced such 'blasts of adversity', owing to the fighting. Perhaps it is after 1671. If so, the day is Tuesday and our clothier is riding towards Huddersfield and not Almondbury, for in that year Huddersfield obtained a licence to hold a weekly Tuesday market. Standing at the foot of many Pennine valleys, it was easier of access than Almondbury, and so soon became more frequented.

Yes, it is after 1671, for here is our clothier dismounting by the church in Huddersfield. A good many other clothiers are there already, and the church wall is almost covered by their pieces, for it is on the church wall that they display their wares. Our weaver is lucky and soon sells his kersey; then he goes to look for the wooldriver and buys four stones (56 pounds) of wool. His poorer neighbour has been before him and bought one stone of wool, which he is carrying to his upland cottage on his back. Their richer neighbour does not buy wool in small quantities in the local market, but travels about to the bigger Yorkshire fairs, and even to the best wool-producing county in England, far-off Lincolnshire.

Our clothier reaches home that evening, and early next morning, with the assistance of his wife and family, sets to work on his fresh stock of wool. He spreads it out on the house floor, tosses it with sticks and picks out any bits of foreign matter in it, and then perhaps dyes it in his lead dyeing vat, which stands outside his door. Then the wool is thoroughly

Children carding wool

oiled—our clothier may use butter for this purpose. Then it is carded, teased into a flossy sliver, by hand of course. Hand-cards were made in pairs, and consisted of sharpened bent iron pins, set in leather and mounted on wooden backs with handles, so that they looked like a pair of iron hairbrushes. Iron was handy, so there were many local card-makers in the West Riding for our weaver to buy cards from—there are many there still, today, who make the great carding machines. Now our weaver's wool is ready to be spun. Most likely it will be a spinster, a woman spinner, who will spin it, and very likely it will be our weaver's wife who will spin most of it, just as it will probably be his children whose hands will do the carding. In the early days of the industry the wool was spun on a distaff, but by the sixteenth century the spin-ning-wheel was prevalent. Spinning by hand, whether by distaff or wheel, is a slow business, and while our weaver would probably keep his spinning in his family to save expense, the richer clothier would put his spinning out to be done by women (widows and spin-sters) in the neighbouring

Spinster at the great wheel

The handthrown shuttle of a seventeenth-century loom

houses, or even much further afield. In 1588 it was estimated that it took forty spinners and carders to supply eight weavers, so spinsters were in great demand.

To make the yarn weave more easily the hanks or bobbins of weft were dipped into the nearby stream, then to shake out the water they were 'wuzzed' round in a basket slung from a stick, one end of the stick being inserted into a 'wuzzing hole' in the nearest field wall. The wall was useful for another purpose, too, for after the yarn had been warped and sized, the warp was hung on sticks protruding from the wall, to dry. When our weaver has finished weaving his piece he lays it on the floor and tramples into it such ammoniacal liquid as he can get, usually human and animal excrement, then throws it across his donkey's back and takes it down to the fulling mill in the valley to be cleansed by scouring, then carries it back home again to be dried and burled. Again it goes to the fulling mill, and is placed in the fulling stocks with soap, which reduces its dimensions. At the fulling mill it is measured and sealed by the Ulnager.

Stretching a wet kersey on the tenter

Then home once more, and the still-dripping cloth is fastened to those long wooden frameworks in the field beside the weaver's door, which we call tenters. As the cloth is fastened to the tenter-hooks, the family pull on it to lengthen it. I suppose it is human nature to stretch the cloth sometimes a little further than it ought to go, by hand or by the broad beam on its lower edge; at any rate down through the centuries come occasional echoes of complaints about 'deceitful' cloths which have been over-tentered. 'Giants to the eye, but dwarfs in the use thereof,' complains one writer of some cloths in the seventeenth century, while another remarks bitterly: 'If a gentleman make a liverie for his man, in the first shower of rain it may fit his Page for Bigness!' At one time a law was passed forbidding any use of the tenter. Since untentered cloth would be unkempt and uneven, however, the law was resisted fiercely, and eventually was modified to permit tentering within specified limits.

When our weaver's piece comes off the tenter, it is Tuesday again, and time to ride to market.

Our weaver does not 'finish' his piece himself; he sells it in this condition, just off the tenters, to the merchant at

Huddersfield market, who will have it dressed to suit himself, possibly at the nearby fulling mill. In the finishing process, the cloth had its nap raised by means of teasel-heads mounted on handles, then it was spread on a curved shearing board and its rough nap cropped by huge shears, to wield which required both strength and skill. After this came perching, mending and pressing.

In the early days of the industry these finishing processes were always carried out at the fulling mills. We have seen that a 'walker' was the same as a fuller, and the shears for cropping the nap were originally called walkers' shears. When the industry grew, and the yeoman clothiers flourished, the richer clothiers carried on every process of the industry under their own roof. But the smaller clothiers, having neither the skill nor the tools nor the time to do this, took their cloth to market undressed. To supply the merchants' demand for finishing near at hand, 'croppers' shops' gradually grew up in the towns, where they were near their customers.

For the richer clothiers, who kept apprentices and employed outside spinners, the local markets were not enough, and they sent their cloth to sell in London, at the weekly cloth market at Blackwell Hall and the yearly cloth fair held on St. Bartholomew's Day. They might perhaps go themselves to London once a year at Bartholomew's tide, but it was impossible to take so long a journey (three or four days on horseback) very frequently, so they sent their cloth by pack-horse carrier to London and employed agents, called cloth factors, there to sell it for them. On one occasion, in 1636, an Ulnager pounced on a pack-horse train travelling to London and seized some cloth from it which he said had not been sealed. The West Riding merchants in this period exported cloth, too, sending it by ship from Hull to all parts of the continent of Europe. In the seventeenth century, when England and Holland were fighting for the mastery of the seas, these ships had to be convoyed to their destination, and great was the vexation of the West Riding when their carrier missed a convoy's departure by unpunctuality, great the indignation when a ship full of broadcloth and kerseys was sunk by enemy action.

In the eighteenth century the cloth trade in the West Riding went forward in long swift strides.

This was due to several causes: some national and some local. To take the national causes first: the export trade of the whole country increased tremendously in this period, owing largely to the development of British settlements overseas. Canada, India, the North American 'colonies', as they were then, formed ever-expanding sources of raw material and markets for British products, while in Europe the struggle for naval supremacy was over, and merchant ships could journey safely across the seas. The home market also expanded because the home population was increasing rapidly, so that the buyers were there in plenty if the clothiers could reach them and could please them.

As regards reaching customers, the eighteenth century helped the clothier by tremendous development of two important means of communication: the turnpike road and the canal. Clothiers and landowners joined together to find the money and get permission from Parliament for these schemes. They subscribed to build the roads and dig the canals, then recouped themselves by tolls from those who used them. In 1759 a turnpike road was brought from Lancashire over Stanedge Moor to Marsden, and down the Colne Valley into Huddersfield, thus changing the valley, as one of its historians has remarked, from a cul-de-sac into a corridor. Even more important was the opening of canals, for since one horse dragging a barge on a canal could pull as much weight as six hundred pack-horses could carry, the saving in time and labour by the use of canal transport was immense. By 1758 the Calder River was made navigable as far as Cooper's Bridge, and then a canal was constructed

DEANHEAD

A woollen-manufacturing hamlet which flourished
in the seventeenth century

*Inset shows cropping shop, remains of fulling mill, and
the breached reservoir*

from that point to the King's Mill. When this was finished, there was an uninterrupted waterway from Huddersfield to Hull—the Colne Valley clothier need no longer rely on carriers and pack-horses to get his cloth to the ship sailing for Holland. He surely wished that the canal could be extended all the way up the Colne Valley and through to Lancashire, but how was it to mount the gradients and cross the Pennine Chain? At that time the engineers could not give the answer, and it was the next century before the hills were tunnelled and the canal went through.

The local cause of the great expansion of the cloth trade in Yorkshire was the introduction there of the worsted trade, which hitherto had belonged almost entirely to East Anglia.

In case this comes to the hands of readers who are not 'in textiles', I had perhaps better explain in non-technical terms the difference between worsted and woollen cloths. Woollen cloths were (and are) woven of soft yarn, spun from wool carded but not combed. By carding, the maze of short curly fibres of the wool are made to hook into each other criss-cross—like the Yorkshire hills. Such woollen cloth felted itself into a strong matted mass beneath the hammering stocks of the fulling mill. The worsted cloths which began now to be made in Yorkshire were woven of smooth thin strong yarn, spun from combed wool, whose long fibres, combed out straight and parallel by a woolcomber using a heated comb, did not felt or interlock when spun but twined snakily round each other. This worsted cloth was strong from the tension of the yarn; it was not, of course, fulled; and the weavers were able to make clear delicate patterns in it from yarn dyed in the wool. The manufacture of this worsted cloth was a novelty for Yorkshire; it did not oust the woollen cloth manufacture, but grew beside it.

How the weaving of worsted was first begun in the West Riding we do not know. Perhaps some East Anglian manu-facturers came north and settled in the West Riding, where water was so abundant; perhaps the West Riding clothiers, finding that their continental customers were beginning to weave woollen cloth for themselves, determined to capture the worsted trade and sent weavers to East Anglia to learn it. Learn it they did, at all events, and their trade increased enormously in consequence. By 1770 the West Riding worsted output was equal to that of Norwich, and Yorkshire worsteds went to Turkey and Astrakhan. One great clothier who lived on a hillside a couple of valleys away from the Colne, had a yearly turnover of twenty thousand pounds ($100,000) in 1737. We still have this clothier's pattern book in Yorkshire, and a wonderful piece of work it is. The little squares of cloth have the most attractive names (birdseyes, amens, callimancoes, tammys), the daintiest designs and all the colours of the rainbow, and beside them Mr. Samuel Hill, clothier, has made his comments. '1,200 bales of this provided in one year for St. Petersburg', he writes beside a clear blue, and beside another: 'The most perfect cloth made in this kingdom'. It seems he did not lack conceit— but his turnover justified it! Mr. Hill's brother-in-law, Joseph Holroyd, was a cloth factor or agent, who bought cloth from Yorkshire clothiers for merchants both in London and in Holland. (Later he settled as a resident in Holland.) A portion of the letter-books of these two men, in which they took copies of the letters they wrote, is still in a Yorkshire museum, and from this we can see the magnitude of the orders Holroyd was placing and Hill was carrying out. Two hundred and fifty pieces form one order for a good customer in Rotterdam.

Of course Hill did not weave all these pieces himself, or even have them woven in his house. He employed men to weave for him. He bought wool and put it out to spin, and then weavers fetched it to their homes on their donkeys, returning the woven pieces to him by the same transport. An old firm in the Colne Valley district, who have records

31

of cloth-making in their family in an unbroken line from 1541, still own a field behind their mill called 'th' owld Neddy-field', which, being translated, means 'the old donkey field'. It is a relic of the days when the weaver's donkey (whom we first met in a court case in 1275) played an essential part in the domestic cloth manufacture system. When the master-clothier received his weaver's pieces, he marketed them.

Naturally a low wall round a churchyard was not a good enough market for such a volume of trade, and so in this century we find Cloth Halls and Piece Halls being erected all over the West Riding. A fine large Cloth Hall was built in Huddersfield in 1766. This Cloth Hall was a striking example of a graceful building perfectly adapted to its purpose, for it consisted of a one-storeyed (later, two-storeyed) arcade built round a practically circular court. The main hall of the building was built along the shorter axis of this oval, and within this hall stood, in 'streets', the benches or stalls on which the cloth was displayed. The covered arcade was divided into many small numbered rooms, each lighted from the inside of the circle by one window, and these rooms

Business in the Main Hall, Cloth Hall, Huddersfield

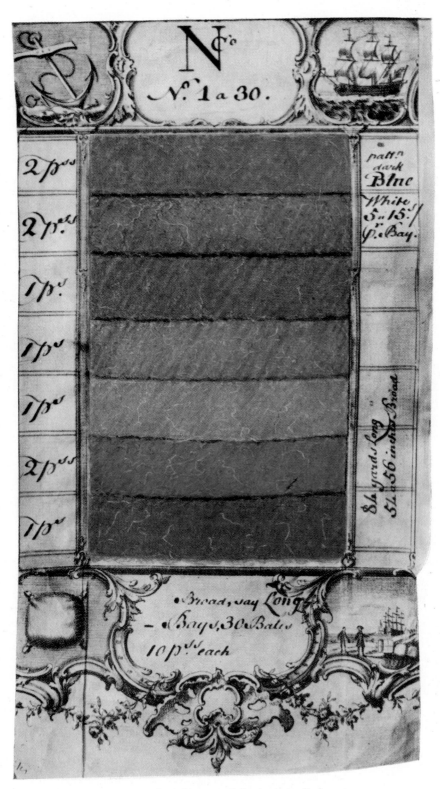

An eighteenth-century clothier's pattern book

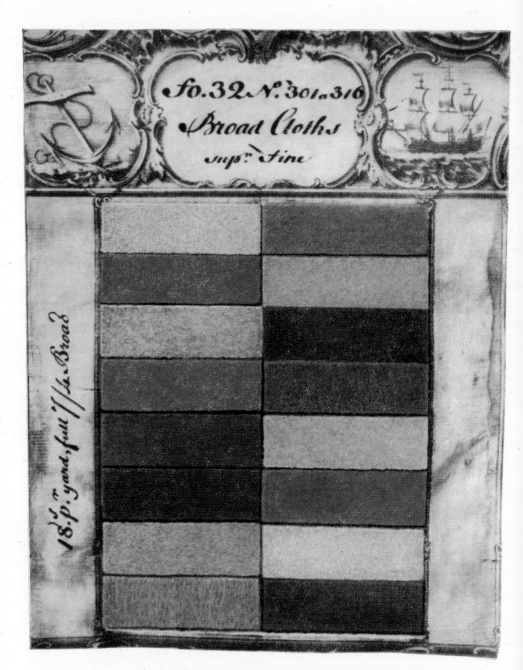

Another page from the eighteenth-century clothier's pattern book

were rented to clothiers, more than one of whom sometimes shared a room. A corridor ran round the outside of these rooms, or booths as they were called, so that a buyer could pass rapidly round, looking in at the wares in each room. There were no windows on the outside of the hall—this was arranged to prevent loss by theft and minimize risk by fire. Above the main entrance stood a small bell-tower. The Cloth Hall was built by Sir John Ramsden, a landowner who at that time owned most of the land in Huddersfield town. The neighbouring clothiers were troubled be-

Estimating the width of the corridor

cause they feared the passages of the Hall were being built too narrow, and a deputation went to Sir John to ask him to have them made wider. A Colne Valley clothier from Milnsbridge, a very broad man, was amongst the deputation; he showed how a piece of cloth was carried on the shoulder, and Sir John measured the width from his left shoulder to his extended right elbow, and ordered that the passages should be made twice that width with a little to spare, so that two men each carrying a piece could pass each other.

Very strict rules were observed at the Cloth Hall. The hours for bringing in the cloth were from 8.30–10 a.m., after which the doors were closed and the clothiers within arranged their wares. Presently a bell was rung, the merchants and factors then entered and made a round of the rooms and stalls, carrying in their hands patterns they wished to match, notes of the pieces they wished to order. They leaned across the wooden trestles on which the cloth was displayed, and bargained with the clothiers in whispers, so that the neighbouring clothiers should not know each other's business. A bell sounded to warn them that only a few minutes of market time remained; then the clock struck half-past twelve, the bell sounded again, and the market was over. The Hall closed, to open again at 3 p.m., when the pieces sold could be taken away by the buyer. Meanwhile the merchants and clothiers had dinner at the Pack Horse Inn nearby, perhaps, where they had stabled their horses. There were 150 stalls in Huddersfield Cloth Hall, but 600 manufacturers regularly brought their wares to be sold there.

That is a long step forward from the twenty-one clothiers who marketed at Almondbury in 1473. But as regards the organization of the cloth trade, it is a step along exactly the same road. Bigger markets, better means of communication, more artistic designs, more distant customers; but no radical changes either in process or in use of labour. The tools which a Yorkshire clothier left by will to his family in 1576, the loom, the spinning-wheel, the shears and shear-board, the tenter ropes, might seem of rather clumsy and antiquated pattern to the weaver of 1756, but he still used the same tools and called them by the same names, still wove his cloth by hand on his own loom at home. The cloth trade was still organized on the Domestic System.

Within the next few years all that was to change.

Kay's flying shuttle, 1733, showing arrangement of cords and pickers for driving shuttle through the warp

III. MACHINES AND MEN

MACHINERY came, and the Colne Valley world was turned upside down.

We cannot claim that the inventions which revolutionized the cloth trade originated in Yorkshire. They came from the county on the other side of the Pennines, Lancashire, and were created for that county's newly developed trade, the manufacture of cotton goods. Then the news of these inventions spread over the Pennine Hills and down the Yorkshire valleys, and the inventions were seen to be applicable to the manufacture of woollen cloth, and were adapted to that purpose.

The first of these inventions was Kay's flying shuttle. This was a simple enough device, consisting merely of a couple of small wooden or leather hammers, one at each side of the loom-gate, worked by cords held in the weaver's hand. The shuttle was mounted on four small wheels, so that when the weaver pulled on the right-hand cord and the hammer

35

struck the shuttle, it rolled rapidly across the loom-gate, and the same in reverse with the left-hand cord and hammer. Kay, a Lancashire man who lived about fifteen miles from the head of the Colne Valley, in Bury, patented the flying shuttle in 1733. Thirty years later, in 1763, it had been adapted by the woollen weavers and was in extensive use in Yorkshire. Not only did it accelerate weaving, but also enabled one man working alone to weave cloths broader than the stretch of his arms.

Since Kay's shuttle enabled the weaver to weave more rapidly, this invention put the weaver even further ahead of the yarn output than before. We have seen that it took five spinners to keep one weaver supplied; now the proportion of spinners to weavers was still further multiplied, and it became urgently necessary to find some way of increasing the spinner's output. Accordingly much thought was given to this problem, and by 1770 Hargreaves, another Lancashire man, invented the spinning jenny. When we first meet this invention in the Holmfirth district about 1776, it could spin eighteen threads at a time; soon the number of spindles increased to forty. It was worked by hand at first, and was not too cumbrous to stand in a corner of the spinner's cottage and the clothier's homestead.

So now the process of cloth manufacture was much accelerated. The clothier's wife could spin more yarn and the clothier weave more cloth than before; the clothier was able to take several pieces to market every week. No longer did all he earn go on wool for the next week's piece and the next week's food; he had a surplus—that is to say, he accumulated capital. He used this capital to employ still more spinners and weavers to make still more cloth, and thus he accumulated still more capital. So the cloth manufacturer prospered and the trade grew. The spinners and weavers still plied their craft in their own homes, but the character of the manufacturer's home changed somewhat.

The yeoman clothier and his family at work in the loom-chamber

He did not himself weave now, nor his wife spin; he busied himself buying the wool and distributing it, perhaps riding round the cottages of the weavers in his employ to see that the cloth was woven in time, then taking the cloth to market. Presently, he began not always to take his cloth to market. He liked to keep his patterns secret and exclusive, not exposed to competitors' gaze at the Cloth Hall; he liked, too, to weave to a merchant's order, so that there was no risk of missing his sale. Better, perhaps, to sell by pattern only, through a cloth factor. The two systems of open market and private order went on side by side for almost a century, but eventually the Cloth Hall was ousted, and the clothier's home became a warehouse. Soon he began to take a room in an inn near the Cloth Hall on Market Day in which to show his best goods privately, and later still he built a fine, handsome warehouse in the town. But this is to go ahead too rapidly. It is still 1779, and a clothier of Honley, drawing up an inventory of his goods prior to making his will, includes looms for both woollen and worsted yarn, a spinning jenny and some tenters—also a 'large Bibell' and a map of America on the wall.

Next year the invention which really 'turned the world upside down' appeared in the Colne Valley. It was the carding machine invented by another Lancashire man, Arkwright.

Perhaps the word 'carding' is not used by the textile trade in all parts of the world, so let us remind ourselves what the process of carding implies. Hitherto, before Arkwright's invention, a child had taken in each hand a tool like a hairbrush, with bristles represented by bent iron pins. Wool or cotton in its rough state was placed on one of these 'cards', and then brushed off, so to speak, on to the other, and so on, back and forth, until the fibre was all teased out into a soft white gauze. Now Arkwright devised cylinders rolling against a large central cylinder, all of which, covered with the iron cards, by rolling against each other carded the cotton into soft continuous sheets. The Yorkshire clothiers found that this carding machine could be used not only for carding wool but for the process known as 'scribbling', whereby, as a Yorkshireman of a previous century described it, 'different colours in dyed wool are delicately mixed'. The children who used to card by hand were now set to take off the cardings and scribbled wool from these machines. At first these carding and scribbling machines were worked by hand, then a horse was used to supply the power; before long, by a natural transition, they were moved down to the fulling mill in the valley, where water-power could be used to turn them by attaching them to the shaft of the water-wheel.

Thus the scribbling mill was born, a development of immense importance in the history of the cloth trade. At first it was a public mill, like the old corn mills and fulling mills; clothiers took their wool to be scribbled and carded as they had taken their corn to be ground and still took their cloth to be scoured and fulled, paying the miller (in Yorkshire speech 'milner') for the service. Then some clothiers began to build scribbling mills for themselves, to save the continual journeyings to and fro between weaving-place and mill, and when scribbling and carding and weaving and scouring and fulling are gathered together beneath one roof, there is the modern factory in all but steam-power.

Outsteps at High Kinders, Greenfield

THE WHEEL

Cog Hole, last of the water-driven scribbling mills

So the Colne Valley world was turned upside down, for the population moved from the upland to the valley. Hitherto the upland had held the houses and the roads and the valley was quiet except at the bridge by the fulling mill; now the uplands began to be quiet and for the first time in its history the Colne Valley began to be dotted by mills along the river. An old map of the 1770s shows fifty-four mills on the Colne and its tributaries, and in the next twenty years or so this number doubled. There were mills at Meltham, at Honley, at Crosland, at Slaithwaite, at Netherton, at Armitage Bridge; there was a mill called Ottiwells Mills at Marsden.

The name of this mill brings us to the most exciting, dramatic, and tragic episode in the whole Colne Valley history.

The next textile invention to invade the valley was the cropping-frame. This was a clumsy, even uncouth-looking affair, consisting of a pair of hand cropping-shears clamped to a grooved iron frame, which was to stand beside the cropping 'bench' or table on which the cloth was laid. At the side of the frame was a wheel, which when turned by hand or power caused the shears, by means of various shafts and ropes, to crop the nap of the cloth, at the same time moving slowly along the frame till it took in the whole length of the cloth. Clumsy device though it was, the cropping-frame, tended by one man, could do the work of ten skilled hand-croppers. In 1812 Enoch and James Taylor, who were originally blacksmiths, but by skill and ingenuity worked themselves up into machine-makers, began to make these frames at Marsden, and some of the local cloth dressers and manufacturers determined to use them. Amongst these manufacturers was Mr. William Horsfall of Ottiwells Mills, Marsden.

To understand the bitterness of the struggle which followed, it is necessary to know something of the world history in this year 1812. At this time England was engaged in her long, bitter, and at times almost desperate struggle against Napoleon, and was in 1812 also at war with the United States, which, owing to certain resentments between the two countries, had taken Napoleon's side. Napoleon was determined to starve England out by a form of blockade which consisted in forbidding British ships to enter all ports under his control and all British goods to travel in any but British ships under pain of confiscation. Since Napoleon controlled most of Europe at that time, both import and export were thus made exceedingly difficult, often almost impossible. Trade was, therefore, very bad, and the cloth trade, with its large volume of export, particularly so; unemployment was rife and bankruptcies frequent. Also, by a most unfortunate chance, the harvests in 1810 and 1811 were singularly bad, so that in 1812 corn was at starvation-high prices.

When the English manufacturer, therefore, faced as he was with high war taxation and fearful loss of trade if he continued the war, and an unthinkable loss of liberty if he tamely

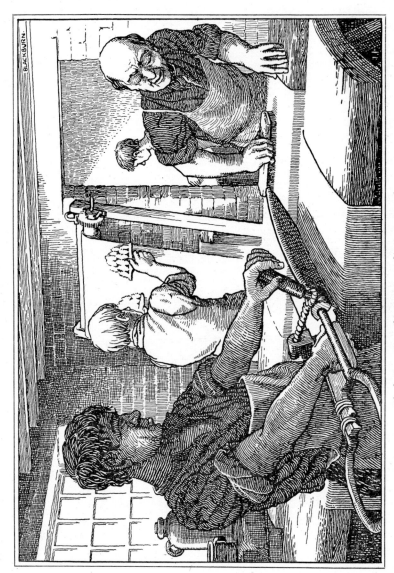

Cloth Dressing: the interior of a cropping shop

abandoned the Napoleonic struggle, saw a way of cheapen-
ing his product and thus cutting his losses and possibly
expanding his home market, he naturally grasped at it
tenaciously. These new frames might save him from bank-
ruptcy, so these new frames he must and would have—
even if he had to ride through blood to his saddle-girths to
do it, as the vehement Mr. Horsfall rather too often an-
nounced incautiously. The English workman, on the other
hand, already under the shadow of unemployment and
unable to buy enough of the dear (because scarce) corn to
sustain himself and his family, was now faced with the
prospect of being thrown out of work and indeed completely
superseded by these accursed frames, as he regarded them;
he therefore determined to resist the frames to the last, and
was all the more reckless because he had little to lose by his
conduct, since starvation or poor relief probably awaited
him in any case.

One type of frame had been adapted to knitting stockings,
and was put into use in Nottingham. The workers there
resented it turbulently and smashed the frames. Their leader
was either named or known as Ned Lud, and his followers
were called Luddites. The movement to resist the hated
frames spread north into Yorkshire, and every district in the
West Riding had its King Lud or General Lud and its group
of Luddites.

The King Lud of the Colne Valley was a young man
named George Mellor, a cropper who worked in his step-
father's cloth-dressing shop at Longroyd Bridge. Mellor was
only twenty-two years old, with fair curly hair, fluent and
vigorous. Two companions in the same shop, of much the
same age, Benjamin Walker and Thomas Smith, and another
young cropper, William Thorpe, from a nearby shop,
formed with Mellor the nucleus of the local Luddites, of
whom there were perhaps thirty or forty, in close touch
with neighbouring groups, Mellor being chief for the whole

John Wood's cropping shop, demolished in 1891

district. The Luddites met at remote inns high up on the Marsden moors, where they took an oath never to betray each other under pain of being 'blotted out of existence'. They called the taking of this oath being 'twissed in', meaning that by this oath they were twisted into one fibre with their fellow croppers. They wrote threatening letters to manufacturers who were putting frames into their mills; they blacked or masked their faces and visited the lonelier homesteads to secure arms, with which they then drilled on the moors. In collecting these arms they were guilty of some acts of violence as well as of robbery, and whenever they could come easily at frames by night, they smashed them. Soldiers were sent to the district to maintain order, but as they did not know against whom they had to operate, their task was difficult. Moreover, the jingle of their harness as they rode out from Marsden on patrol could be heard miles away across the quiet moors, and as they were strangers and the croppers knew every moorland path from birth, the croppers were in the valley when the redcoats climbed the hill, and vice versa. The croppers had a song of their own, which ran:

44

Come, cropper lads of high renown,
Who love to drink good ale that's brown,
And strike each haughty tyrant down,
  With hatchet, pike and gun!

  (*Chorus*) Oh, the cropper lads for me,
        Who with lusty stroke,
        The shear frames broke,
        The cropper lads for me.

What though the specials still advance,
And soldiers nightly round us prance,
The cropper lads still lead the dance,
  With hatchet, pike and gun!

  (*Chorus*) Oh, the cropper lads for me, etc.

And night by night when all is still
And the moon is hid behind the hill
We forward march to do our will
  With hatchet, pike and gun!

  (*Chorus*) Oh, the cropper lads for me, etc.

Great Enoch still shall lead the van,
Stop him who dare! Stop him who can!
Press forward every gallant man
  With hatchet, pike and gun!

  (*Chorus*) Oh, the cropper lads for me,
        Who with lusty stroke,
        The shear frames broke,
        The cropper lads for me.

The Enoch referred to in the last verse was not a man, but
a huge smith's hammer with which the croppers broke
the frames. It suited their sardonic humour to say: 'Enoch

45

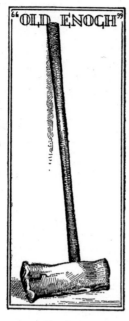

"OLD ENOCH"

makes them and Enoch breaks them', in allusion to Enoch Taylor's name.

The croppers were successful in breaking up a load of frames crossing the Liversedge moor, some six miles to the north-east of Huddersfield; emboldened by this success and angered by the persistence of the manufacturer concerned, they made a night attack on his mill which turned almost into a pitched battle. Firearms were used on both sides; several Luddites were seriously wounded, and two died. The Luddites were considerably daunted, and the manufacturers correspondingly elated, by this episode. Mellor was furious, and a fortnight later, on Tuesday 28 April 1812, the King Lud and his three closest companions attacked Mr. Horsfall as he rode homewards from Huddersfield on market day. The clothier's way lay within a few yards of the Longroyd Bridge cropping-shop where the chief Luddites worked, so it is probable Mellor saw him pass; at any rate, the croppers divided into pairs, passed ahead of Horsfall and ambushed him.

At a quarter to six the clothier rode up to a public house on Crosland Moor, had a glass of ale and treated two cloth-hawkers who were standing there, then rode on towards a nearby plantation. Here the Luddites, concealed amid the trees, fired at him from pistols loaded with slugs. Mr. Horsfall fell from his horse severely wounded in the thigh. Another clothier galloped up and, helped by passers-by, carried the wounded man back to the Crosland Moor inn and fetched a surgeon from Huddersfield; but the unfortunate victim died from loss of blood that night. Meanwhile the murderers escaped over the brow into the Holme

Valley, and, hiding their pistols beneath some wool refuse in the house of a clothier cousin of Mellor, made their way back to Longroyd Bridge and constructed alibis.

The authorities made vigorous efforts to discover their identity, but though this was well known to almost every cloth-worker in the Colne Valley, the secret was kept until the autumn of the year, when the murderers were betrayed by one of themselves, Benjamin Walker, for the sake of the £2,000 ($10,000) reward offered. Once the chain of secrecy was broken many Luddites gave themselves up, surrendered their arms and were pardoned—they described this process as 'being untwissed'. Many others were arrested, and wholesale trials took place at York in the January of 1813. The murderers were found guilty, and with the exception of Walker were hanged; many other croppers were transported. A general pardon followed, and the West Riding, shocked by its recent violence, settled down.

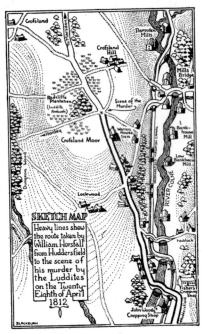

Walker after a short imprisonment was released and returned to the Colne Valley where he lived on to old age, but he was generally shunned and execrated for his treachery as well as his crime.

The frames continued in use, and their design was rapidly improved. The timely mechanizing of English industry, of which the frames were a part, helped England to defeat Napoleon. Two years later, in 1815, he was decisively defeated at Waterloo, and England enjoyed her continental markets again.

47

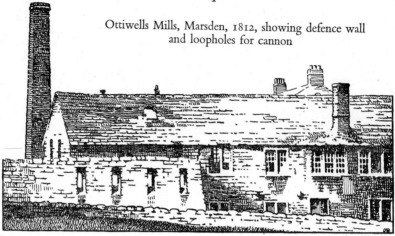

Ottiwells Mills, Marsden, 1812, showing defence wall
and loopholes for cannon

And now the Industrial Revolution was to be completed, the last blow was to fall on the Domestic System, while amongst its ruins arose the Factory System which gave the supremacy in the English cloth trade to Yorkshire.

Already the manufacturers had been grumbling for some time about the uncertainty and uneven volume of the available water power. There were days in the winter when the Colne was in spate, the water, rushing down deep and strong, turning the water-wheels rapidly. There were days in the summer when the river could hardly trickle over its rocky bed; then the water-wheels stood motionless, and the water-driven machines stood motionless too. When one was a farmer as well as a clothier, such idle days could be put to good use on the land, but when one was a manufacturer with a great trade, many employees, and dates to keep with merchants, they were pure loss and exasperation. The manufacturers had tried to get over this difficulty by building reservoirs high up in the hills, from which water could be released down the streams when it was needed in dry seasons; in 1794 a reservoir was built on the moors above Slaithwaite, and as the nineteenth century came in others were constructed about the neighbourhood, for instance, in the

Wessenden Valley above Marsden, and at the head of Merrydale stream and Saddleworth. These regulated the water supply to some extent and kept the machines turning, but the more forward-looking manufacturers turned very gladly to the new invention—Steam.

For now the giant Steam was harnessed to industry; a tremendous new supply of power was made available; one wrote to Messrs. Boulton and Watt, of Birmingham, and sent measurements, and a few months later a boiler and a steam engine came rumbling up the valley on waggons, and one need not worry about the water supply any more. In the 1790s the men in the smaller valleys of the district began to install the new steam engines, for the smallest streams were the most tiresome, because they were the soonest dry. These engines were not intended at first to run the machines all the year round, only in the dry season, but their reliability and even drive soon won the day. The mills along the Colne itself began to run on steam rather later, since the Colne was larger, but from 1820 onwards the throb of the steam engine quivered in the Colne Valley air. There was iron in the county to be moulded into engines and boilers and machines; there was plenty of coal near at hand just over the hill to feed the boiler fire. Now in East Anglia and in the Cotswolds, the previous centres of the trade, there was no nearby coal, no nearby iron. As the power of steam grew, the trade of the West Riding grew, and the trade of the districts far from coal dwindled and sank. When the mill chimneys rose, trade rose; where there were no chimneys tossing out long plumes of smoke, soon there was no trade.

The steam engine drew the worker to the factory. Many workers could have power for their machines supplied by one boiler, which was being employed wastefully if it did not run as many machines as it could; the workers therefore tended to be gathered under one roof. Steam-power was regular, steam-driven machines ran steadily and produced even work. Work

49

done in the factory could receive more supervision from the manufacturer than work done at home, and was subject to fewer delays. All these were great advantages in addition to the supreme advantage of increased output, so, although the workers hated the factory system and fought it at first whenever they could, and although handloom weavers persisted in the outlying districts for another half-century, till the 1850s, factories had come to stay.

They brought, at first, one great evil in their train. In the old days the weavers' children had helped to card the wool, sitting on a low stool by their mothers at home; now, like their fathers, they were drawn into the factories. They were put as 'pieceners' to the scribbling and carding and slubbing machines, which, unfortunately, were of a height suitable to their small stature, and required no more skill than a child's to feed them. Indeed, the children were often in greater demand than the men. A black stain on the West Riding's good name is its exploitation of these children, who were made to toil for incredibly long hours—twelve, thirteen, fifteen hours a day. As they had often walked long miles from their upland homes to the mills in the valley, by evening the poor little things were so exhausted that they slept as they stood, and it is unfortunately true that the overlookers often beat them to keep them awake. The continual standing in one position, the continual crooking of the left arm to hold the cardings, often permanently maimed and bent their tender limbs. All this is confirmed by indisputable evidence before a Parliamentary Commission. But, as this ill treatment is an indelible black mark on West Riding history, so the freeing of the children from this slavery is a bright light, for it was the work chiefly of a West Riding estate

Factory children of 1826

agent, Richard Oastler, and a West Riding cloth manufacturer, John Wood.

A very fine story is related —by Oastler himself, in the magazine which he wrote while imprisoned for debt in later years—of the manner in which he came to take up the children's cause. In the autumn of 1830 Oastler, a man of great humanity, commanding presence and moving eloquence, had been addressing a local meeting in support of William Wilberforce, who was then reaching the successful close of his campaign against West Indian slavery. Oastler dined at Bradford with his friend the cloth manufacturer John Wood, and described with vehemence the iniquities of slavery discussed at the meeting. Suddenly, Wood, who had been sitting silent and thoughtful, interrupted him.

'I wonder, Mr. Oastler,' he said, 'that you do not take up the cause of the children in the mills. There is a slavery in our Yorkshire mills quite as dreadful as any in the Indies.'

Oastler, astonished, asked for details; Wood gave them, begging him to take up the matter in a public campaign. Oastler would make no promise, and the two men parted for the night. It chanced that Oastler had a business appointment very early next morning, and as he rose before dawn, in a dark hour of wind and rain, he suddenly realized with painful force that the children were already at work in the mills. Visiting his host to say farewell, he found Mr. Wood in bed, with a Bible beside him on a table beneath a lighted candle.

Wood, unable to sleep for distress about the mill children, had spent the night in reading the Bible, every line of which, as he said to Oastler, had convinced him more clearly of his duty.

'I will not let you go', he concluded, 'till you have promised to take up the children's cause.'

Oastler thereupon laid his hand on the open Bible, and said with stern conviction: 'I will take up that cause here and now, and promise never to lay it down till the children of England are free'.

He was true to his word. Conducting the campaign in the manner customary in this democratic country, he first wrote a letter to the local newspapers, then held public meetings, then interested Members of Parliament, and repeated these activities until widespread public indignation forced Parliament to pass the Ten Hours Bill, limiting the hours to be worked in the new factories. Throughout Oastler's twelve years' campaign, he received firm and consistent support from the workers in the Huddersfield and Colne Valley district, many of whom marched all the way to York to attend one of the most famous meetings of King Richard, as they called him. Many of the manufacturers hated him at the time for his agitation, and rejoiced when he became bankrupt and was thrown into prison. It is pleasant to remember, however, that when he was an old man, and the West Riding cloth operatives subscribed a penny each to buy him a new suit, a firm of Colne Valley manufacturers gave the cloth free so that the workers' subscriptions might pay for the tailoring, and this action probably represented a general change of heart and understanding of Oastler's mission on the manufacturers' part. A statue of Richard Oastler, with two of the children he saved at his knee, stands in a busy street in Bradford, and his name is remembered with respect and gratitude wherever cloth is woven in Yorkshire. The Ten Hours Bill, passed in 1842, led the way to the many protective regulations passed to secure the cloth operatives' welfare, in the last hundred years. The tradition of collective action in the textile trade thus founded by Oastler was strong amongst the operatives, so that one of the early Trade Unions in England was that of the weavers, founded in 1883, a Masters' Association having been founded the year before.

The machine and the factory had come to stay, and they soon transformed the lower slopes of the Colne Valley from a green, sparsely populated countryside, to a congested industrial area. The Industrial Revolution took the worker away from being his own master in his own home in the fields, and put him in a smoky town working for wages by the clock, but it cheapened the product, extended the market and the worker's purchasing power, and by enriching the community ultimately gave him State education, municipal lighting and water and libraries, the principle of collective bargaining, and the power to mould his world in concert with his fellow citizens, in exchange. The balance of social gain and loss should, perhaps, not be struck yet until we see what the still-newer source of power, electricity, coupled with a more enlightened social conscience, can do to improve our living and working amenities.

As regards the product: The Industrial Revolution extended the use of new cloth from the few to the many.

What of the cloth itself? How did it differ from the handloom cloth, now that it had become the product of machinery?

The advent of tweeds among the sporting fraternity

IV. COLOUR AND DESIGN

THE nineteenth century was a century of invention, and nowhere was invention more prolific than in the cloth trade.

The *Leeds Mercury*, a Yorkshire newspaper which has been in existence since 1718, published, in October 1829, a report on the state of the Huddersfield and district woollen trade, in which occurs the following passage: 'One branch of the fancy trade has, however, been considerably revived by the introduction of a machine called a WITCH, which enables the weaver to beautify the cloth with a great variety of flowers; and this species of goods being new is in considerable demand, and employs a proportionate number of looms'. This Drum Witch loom could lift and depress the warp yarns mechanically, as did another loom invented about the same time, the Dobbie. They thus enabled the weaver to beautify the cloth with flowers, as the newspaper says, or in other words to weave figured cloth, by machine. The figures were at first 'birdseyes', such as old Sam Hill handwove in 1737, i.e. tiny diamonds, then, as skill increased, small flowers, at first not larger than a five-cent piece.

In 1830 a Jacquard loom was shown in a Huddersfield inn by a Frenchman, and was eagerly adopted by a manufacturer of the name of Gill, who put up premises on the south side of Almondbury and began to design for his Jacquards in a most enterprising way. The Jacquard was an improved type of figure-weaving loom taking upwards of four hundred warp threads, so that large and elaborate patterns could be woven on it. The designs of Gill's fancy waistcoatings (vestings) were so novel and striking that they eclipsed those of older firms, and since fancy vestings were extremely popular at that time and a highly lucrative 'line', the Huddersfield and Colne Valley district woke to the importance of the designer. A family of French Huguenot descent, whose ancestors had come to England as refugees from religious persecution, had settled in Almondbury towards the end of the eighteenth century and produced fine designs for figured silk; now these Etchells turned their attention to woollen materials and helped to infuse elegance into shawls and mantle cloths. But local talent for design proved naturally abundant amongst the Huddersfield and Colne Valley men, whose ancestors had been concerned with textiles for centuries; the demand for designing talent stimulated the supply, and the supply the demand; at the Great Exhibition of 1851 (of which more anon), the designs from this district showed a striking supremacy.

Parallel with these developments in design came an expanding range of colour. Here again the district was lucky in the possession of men of inventive genius. A manufacturer of Almondbury named John Nowell, who lived from 1794 to 1869, with his friend and pupil George Jarmaine made experiments in the dye vat which started a whole dyestuffs industry. Jarmaine lectured on chemistry at the Huddersfield College and the Huddersfield Mechanics' Institute (founded in 1838 and 1843 respectively), with special reference to the chemistry of dyeing, and his pupils, the sons of manufacturers and of operatives, took the colour of his teaching. Two Huddersfield men,

Thomas Holliday and Dan Dawson, were the first to extract colours from coal-tar, despite all continental claims to the contrary. They succeeded in producing the colour mauve in 1856, and their dyestuffs firm progressed rapidly from this initial impetus into a huge industry of international importance.

From the interplay of these two forces, design and colour, came the Colne Valley tweeds of today, with their skilfully placed 'nips', their subtle checks, their brilliant yet delicate and softly blended colourings.

It is difficult to discover exactly when and where the tweeds first made their appearance in the Colne Valley. The word 'tweed' is of Scottish origin, but whether it is derived from the River Tweed or from a miswriting of the word 'tweel', which is Scottish for 'twill', cannot now be settled with any certainty. Sir Walter Scott is said to have set the fashion for tweed by having trousers made from a shepherd's plaid, about the year 1831, and the word 'tweed' is clearly written in a letter from a merchant in 1842. But we must leave these agreeable stories to their birthplace, the home of our friendly competitors across the border. As regards the Colne Valley, some manufacturers say that tweeds were being made there between 1840 and 1850, but since there is only one mention of tweed from the Huddersfield district at the Great Exhibition, it seems likely that this date is rather too early, at any rate for their large-scale manufacture in the neighbourhood.

The Great Exhibition, held in London at the Crystal Palace, a huge erection of glass and steel built for the purpose, was planned by the Prince Consort, Queen Victoria's husband, to stimulate and improve the industries of Great Britain; it was visited by merchants, manufacturers and sightseers from every trade and country in the world, and proved a world-wide stimulus to industry. The official catalogue of the Exhibition, which lists the items displayed by every exhibitor, shows the Huddersfield and Colne Valley manufacturers exhibiting doeskins, drab kerseys, Albert checks, wool plaids

for children's dresses, and, above all, fancy woollen trouser-
ings in great profusion. One Meltham firm shows 'hair-line
for trousers'. 'Hair-line', as every merchant and manufacturer knows, is a 'one and one' design which may fairly be
called a tweed; probably this design was in black and white.

So in 1851 we have the tweed manufacture planted in the
Colne Valley district and just beginning to grow. By 1861 it
figures in a book on the Yorkshire textile trade: 'Tweeds',
says the writer, 'are a light, mixed fabric, suitable for summer
overcoats; they have been made, but not to any great extent,
in this locality'. By the 1870s they were more firmly estab-
lished. A Colne Valley manufacturer, who is still making
tweeds today, told me that he always remembers the first
tweed yarn he ever saw because it was blended by his father
just before he died in 1879. It was for a hair-line of black and
grey. Another Colne Valley manufacturer, the direct descendant of the clothier who was measured from shoulder to
elbow to determine the size of the Cloth Hall passages,
entered his father's business and made tweeds in 1880. One of
the first of his patterns was a three-by-three twill, having a
light brown, seal or grey fancy warp and black weft; another
was a birdseye twill in black and white. At that time he showed
some twenty ranges a year, eight or ten shades in a range.

These were for men's overcoats and men's suits. But soon
tweeds for women's wear began to be made and shown. They
appeared first in 1880, were no longer a novelty in 1884—my
mother wore a tweed skirt to tramp the moors at Meltham
before 1893—but did not win the popular favour till the turn
of the century. In 1900 a big exhibit of fancy tweeds for
women appeared in the Paris Exhibition, and from then on-
ward they progressed in rapid strides. Some Paris firms began
to make 'tailor-mades' for women, of Scottish and Yorkshire
tweeds, in 1902, and a year or two later the great French
dress designer Poiret brought out the short skirt, which, as a
tweed representative of then and now exclaims in a letter,

'Revolutionized the trade! Killed the ladies' boot trade, brought in shoes and silk stockings and no more underskirts!!!! And incidentally brought the length for a lady's costume down to three yards or even less instead of five-and-a-half, which was a revolution in itself.'

Whether the emancipation of women produced the short skirt, or the short skirt the emancipation of women, is perhaps more of a question than this very knowledgeable representative chooses to indicate, but certainly, looked at from the tweed angle, there were many circumstances in the first decade of this century favourable to the ladies' tweed trade. The week-end habit, the shooting parties favoured by King Edward VII, at which, for men and women alike, tweeds were correct wear, the new bicycling craze, as well as advances in medical hygiene, psychology and social ideas generally, all helped forward the discovery that three yards were lighter to carry than five-and-a-half, and that if women displayed their ankles in public the world did not disintegrate but, on the contrary, seemed rather pleasanter. In 1910 Mrs. Asquith, wife of the then Prime Minister, on behalf of a charity held a show of Poiret's models at 10 Downing Street. Amongst these models were walking suits for ladies in English tweeds and English worsteds. The tweeds made a hit, and from that day tweed suits in varying but plain and practical styles have formed a normal part of the well-dressed woman's wardrobe, whatever her income bracket. The richness and variety of the tweed's colour and design continually increased, as manufacturers strove to excel their competitors and capture the market, until today very large sums are spent yearly by every manufacturer on the preparation of his designs, in whose number and variety he takes legitimate pride.

The coming of this variety of colour and design to the cloth trade revolutionized its methods of sale. We already saw in 1737 that Sam Hill, that highly successful individualist, did much of his business direct with merchants or through a cloth factor who acted as their agent, preferring this method to that of the Cloth Hall. When woollens and worsted both became machine-made fancy goods, the cloth still needed to be shown to customers so that they might appreciate its beauties, but the manufacturer no longer wished to take it to open market, for there his competitor would see it and be able to copy his designs, reproducing them quickly and in bulk on his machine-run looms. Even if simple imitation were not resorted to, any novelty exhibited was sure to start a train of thought and invention in the competing designer's head, which the manufacturer preferred to confine to his own.

Accordingly, the Cloth Hall's usefulness began to dwindle. Already, in 1822, more than a hundred manufacturers of fancy goods were using private rooms in inns and houses near the Cloth Hall to display their wares, and as the trade prospered, as the range of colour widened and designs grew more complex, the manufacturers of both woollen and worsteds built huge impressive warehouses in which to show their cloths privately to their customers. Soon after 1870 the stalls in the Huddersfield Cloth Hall—a century earlier thought so commodious and convenient—began to empty, and the same phenomenon was observable in the Cloth and Piece Halls all over the West Riding. The Halls lingered on, slipping gradually from their high estate as centres of the cloth trade into mere offices and sometimes mere vegetable markets. In 1930 the Huddersfield Cloth Hall was pulled down to make room for a cinema.

But to return to the nineteenth century, when the need for private marketing on a large scale first arose. The cloths were in the manufacturer's warehouse, beautifully arranged on impressive mahogany counters for the merchant to see and feel, but the warehouse was in Huddersfield and the merchant, especially the export merchant, was often in London. Thus the London office, the system of pattern lengths, and the London representative came into being. My own grandfather was the London representative of a large textile manufacturing firm in the 1870s. My mother draws a wonderful picture of him, with his long brown Dundreary whiskers smoothly brushed and parted accurately to a hair, his top hat and frock coat, then the uniform of business men in London, his elegant umbrella and lemon gloves. In those days the London representation of a big textile firm was a plum in the textile world; my grandfather was a dandy as well as a chapel deacon.

Presently, the manufacturer grew restless about the export houses. Intermediaries were satisfactory for large-scale sales of single-patterned products, but his own complex goods depended for their charm on their great range and variety. Could he not sell his wares better to the merchant abroad if he saw him face to face? Some of the larger, older firms already had members of the family resident abroad; there had been cousins in New York, Amsterdam and St. Petersburg since the end of the eighteenth century, and the practice was clearly profitable. A resident representative in every land was too great a luxury to be thought of in those less-lavish days, but why not extend the range of your commercial traveller? Accordingly, direct representation overseas was inaugurated, and soon individual travellers were as well known to business men in the United States, South America, China and Canada, as they were to merchants in Edinburgh or London.

The travelling representative has done much to cultivate the international reputation of Colne Valley cloth, and the manufacturer, by giving honest value and fixed prices to one and all, whether far or near, has supported that reputation. The British cloth manufacturer strives to deserve and achieve a name for straightforwardness and integrity. His goods are up to sample. He desires no unfair advantages, but is content to rest his appeal to the markets of the world on the quality and attractiveness of his cloth.

In cloth and men, Colne Valley quality has achieved world renown

V. QUALITY TELLS

QUALITY tells, both in cloth and men. England and the textile trade have both suffered very strong 'blasts of adversity' during the last fifty years, but both have high hopes of weathering them by staunch adherence to a certain high standard of quality and conduct.

The protective McKinley tariff imposed by the U.S.A. in 1890 was a blow under which the West Riding textile trade reeled, the total export of cloth dropping between 1890 and 1894 from 63,000,000 to 19,000,000 running yards. It was gloomily prophesied at that time that grass would grow in the streets of the West Riding towns, and I have heard manufacturers today speak of seeing their fathers close rows of weaving sheds at a stroke in 1890, as one of their most tragic experiences. Gradually, however—as so often happens with tariffs—the price of the goods within the tariff wall rose towards the level of those outside, and the Yorkshire product began to make its way again by sheer quality. The Dingley tariff struck another blow, but from 1902 to 1907 the export of cloth from England to the world averaged 27,000,000 (running) yards a year.

Then came the First World War. From 1914 to 1918 the West Riding turned aside from its peacetime product, to make khaki and Navy and Air Force blue, not only for Great Britain, but for all the Allies. Millions and millions of yards came off the Yorkshire looms to clothe the Allied forces, and these millions of yards were woven by 'diluted' labour. The young men were in the Army, the Navy, the Royal Flying Corps (as the Air Force was then called); it was left to the over-age men and the women to carry on the trade. The day in 1919 when the first coloured piece for four years came off a Colne Valley loom, woven to be worn at the wedding of the manufacturer's daughter, was indeed a day of rejoicing for the West Riding.

A post-war 'boom' followed. The world had seen no West Riding cloth for four years, and was eager to resume its reception; orders poured in upon the delighted manufacturers from all corners of the earth. The operatives—those at least who did not lie buried in France and Flanders—returned to their peacetime tasks. Cloth poured from the looms, money poured into (and out of) manufacturers' and operatives' pockets; everyone was prosperous, everyone could afford a new suit; the wheels of industry spun faster and faster, from 1918 to 1921.

Then there came a sudden change. This is not the place for a discussion of the economic and political causes of the post-war slump; they did not concern the textile trade alone, but were deep and world-wide, embracing the economic collapse of Central Europe, war debts, the bank rate, and the accumulation of gold amongst other factors. It is enough to say that whereas in 1920 textile prices were high and trade booming, in 1921

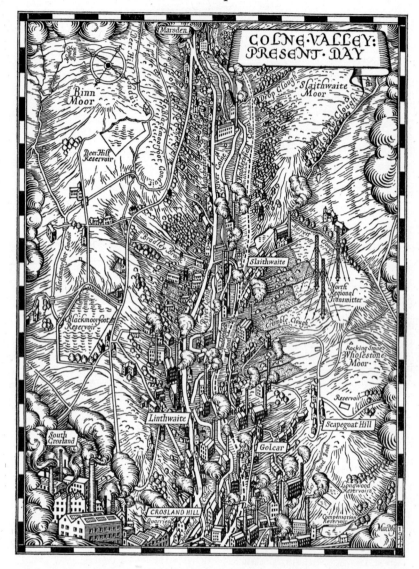

there was such a slump (though not in the trade with U.S.A.) that prices could scarcely be said to exist at all. The Excess Profits Duty, paid on all wartime profits which exceeded the recent peacetime average of the firm, was increased from sixty per cent to eighty per cent in the 1921 Budget, causing a general dismay. Wool buyers at the Australian wool sales felt a sudden lack of confidence, and did not buy in their customary quantities. The price of wool thereupon fell. The buyers then held off more than ever, in the expectation that the price would fall still more, and this vicious circle continued until the price of wool touched rock bottom. The price of yarn followed the price of wool, and the price of cloth followed the price of yarn. In a few months, cloth which had been worth twenty-two shillings and sixpence (then about 4.50 dollars) a yard dropped to five shillings (1 dollar) a yard, and it was not easy to find customers even at that low price. The foreign merchants ceased to send eager cables demanding cloth, and sometimes even repudiated those already sent, since to buy at twenty-two-and-six and sell at five shillings would very soon ruin them.

A protracted agony began in the West Riding for manufacturer and operative alike. The export of cloth fell by nearly 150,000,000 square yards between 1920 and 1921. In that year, out of 54,000 registered workers in the Huddersfield area, 28,000—approximately fifty-two per cent—were unemployed. To keep their businesses going, the manufacturers economized; they decreased their staffs and cut down their personal expenditure; money circulated less rapidly; the purchasing power of the community decreased, and trade inevitably grew worse. Mill buildings, machinery, homes, investments, were mortgaged to the banks; among the manufacturers bankruptcies were frequent, the operatives existed meagrely on Unemployment Insurance Benefit, eked out by the family savings; the spectre of insecurity haunted everyone. A long, tough fight was waged dauntlessly against economic forces which almost proved too strong for the whole industry. Only the soundest finance, the firmest courage, the finest workmanship, could prevail. The textile export figures fluctuated during the next few years, but recovery did not really begin till 1932, Britain having left the gold standard in 1931.

HAROLD BLACKBURN 1944

The view across the Colne Valley at Milnsbridge

Hardly had the West Riding had time to catch its breath, sigh with relief, and begin to smile again, than the menace of Hitlerism appeared on the horizon, a cloud at first small as a man's hand which grew rapidly till it swallowed almost the whole sky. Again, I must not enter upon a political discussion of the causes of the 1939 to 1945 war, but I feel bound to state, for the honour of the West Riding, that many of its citizens—sturdy, stubborn, independent clothiers in 1933 as they had been for many centuries before—perceived the dangers of dictatorship in good time.

The Second World War brought, by degrees as the situation rendered it necessary, complete Governmental control of the textile trade for the duration. There were three main aspects of this control: production (at first) for export, production for the armed forces, and production for the home trade.

In the early days of the war, before Japan's unprovoked attack made the United States a belligerent, when Great Britain was paying for all she bought in U.S.A. on a cash-and-carry basis, the export of cloth to U.S.A. was encouraged by the Government, since the dollars paid by American merchants for English cloth enabled England to buy American munitions. But, after the Lease-Lend principle became operative, by which each of the United Nations contributed freely all she could to a common United Nations pool, the export of cloth to the United States and South America was cut off. Indeed, Britain deliberately sacrificed practically the whole of her export trade in all markets, in all commodities, in order to put the maximum effort into winning the war.

For the armed forces, not only of Great Britain but of all the occupied countries which had personnel in England—Poland, France, Holland, Belgium, Czechoslovakia, Norway—the mills of Great Britain provided uniforms, as well as for some officers of the United States forces under Reverse Lease-Lend. A Colne Valley manufacturer, who entered his father's business in 1880 and has one of the largest concerns in the Valley today, told me that a figure of fifty million running yards of cloth for the armed forces of Great Britain and her Allies during the previous and the recent war would be an understatement. This prodigious output had to be produced under grave labour difficulties, since in the last war years men between eighteen and fifty-five, and women between sixteen and thirty, were always, and women from thirty to fifty sometimes, called to sterner tasks. 180,000 workers went from the textile trade to the war.

Lastly, the Government, acting through the Board of Trade and in conjunction with the textile trade, took steps to ensure that every citizen should be able to buy, within the range of his purchasing power, the necessary minimum of sound and well-cut clothes. The relation in quantity between a manufacturer's bulk cloths and his exclusive wares was controlled, and the price and consistency of the normal bulk cloths was controlled, so that there should always be a sufficiency of reasonably priced cloth, 'utility' cloth, as it was called, to satisfy the needs of citizens in the lower income brackets. The combination of this price control with freedom in design, and with the employment of world-famous dress designers for utility suits and dresses, produced results very agreeable to good sartorial taste. Clothes are still rationed in Great Britain today (1947). Our small ration of clothes coupons does not permit us to buy much cloth wear, but what we buy is well cut, well designed, and well woven.

In 1939 the Colne Valley was a great industrial centre, thickly populated on its lower slopes, forested by mill chimneys, roaring with traffic by road and rail. Travelling down the Valley at dusk in time of peace, you saw great blocks of brilliant light all along the Colne, set at strange angles and different levels in accordance with the contours of hill and stream—the mills, working overtime, with their thousands of looms clacking within. Above them towered the tall slender round chimneys, each with a slender plume of

Sir John Ramsden's canal. The basin at Apsley, 1944

smoke. Follow the smoke to its tip, and you would see—you still will see—tucked into a quiet fold of the distant green hillside the grey stone homestead with the row of mullioned windows in the second storey, where cloth was made by a clothier who rode a pack-horse to Almondbury market hundreds of years ago.

During the war the lights of the Colne Valley mills were curtained for the blackout, the road bore only the necessary minimum of traffic, the young workers were absent on more important errands for the freedom of man, the textile trade was devoted to the stern tasks of war. But now the lights are up again, the workers are returning as rapidly as the tasks of world peace permit, and the textile trade is eager to regain the export markets it voluntarily gave up during the war.

For as everyone knows, export trade is not only a private desirability but a public duty in Britain today. Britain sold her foreign investments during the war to pay for munitions which vanished in smoke in the bombardment of the United Nations' enemies; all she can use now to buy food from overseas is the overseas purchase price of her manufactures. Our exports must earn if we are to eat; we must export or expire.

69

The Colne Valley views this 1947 situation as a stimulus and as a challenge, which it intends to meet with all its textile skill, its highest traditions of quality, its most vigorous enterprise. Cloth has been woven in the Colne Valley certainly for more than six centuries, its structure and pattern changing with the changing needs of the years; the Colne Valley hopes and intends to weave good cloth for many centuries more. As an old poem of the fifteenth century reads:

> For every man must have meat, drink and cloth;
> There is neither pope, emperor nor king,
> Bishop, cardinal, or any man living,
> Of what condition, or what manner degree,
> During their living, they must have things three.
> Meat, drink and cloth.

The Colne Valley is proud to contribute to the supply of one of the three primary human needs.

This book is issued by the Huddersfield and District Woollen Export Group, Chamber of Commerce, Huddersfield, Yorkshire, England, to whom all inquiries should be made. The maps are by Macdonald Gill, the covers and endpapers by Barnett Freedman. It was seen through the press by Sir Francis Meynell and printed at the Curwen Press. William Haigh devised and supervised the whole.